Christmas Present, Christmas Past

Christmas Present, Christmas Past

This journal is for you to capture and share
the magic of your Christmas.

Year after year this decoration can be updated with
your precious memories and photographs telling the
tale of what you did for the festive celebrations and
describing your hopes for the year ahead.

This will become one of your own Christmas traditions
. . . creating a story that will be treasured forever.

This Christmas journal belongs to:

A bit about myself . . .

Christmas Present, Christmas Past

Year _____

Christmas Eve

Where we were . . .

Who was there . . .

Things we talked about & things we did . . .

What we were excited about . . .

Things that made the evening memorable . . .

Bedtime was at . . .

Christmas Day

We woke up at . . .

Where we celebrated . . .

Who was there . . .

What we did . . .

Traditions we followed or started . . .

Some of the memorable presents that were given and received . . .

What we ate and drank . . .

Things that made this Christmas special . . .

Things that made us laugh and smile . . .

What was going on in the wider world?

Reflections & Aspirations

The best moments of the past year . . .

Hopes and wishes for the future . . .

Plans for the coming year . . .

Some of the 'new year' resolutions set . . .

Christmas Present,
Christmas Past

Year _____

Christmas Eve

Where we were . . .

Who was there . . .

Things we talked about & things we did . . .

What we were excited about . . .

Things that made the evening memorable . . .

Bedtime was at . . .

Christmas Day

We woke up at . . .

Where we celebrated . . .

Who was there . . .

What we did . . .

Traditions we followed or started . . .

Some of the memorable presents that were given and received . . .

What we ate and drank . . .

Things that made this Christmas special . . .

Things that made us laugh and smile . . .

What was going on in the wider world?

Reflections & Aspirations

The best moments of the past year . . .

Hopes and wishes for the future . . .

Plans for the coming year . . .

Some of the 'new year' resolutions set . . .

Christmas Present, Christmas Past

Year _____

Christmas Eve

Where we were . . .

Who was there . . .

Things we talked about & things we did . . .

What we were excited about . . .

Things that made the evening memorable . . .

Bedtime was at . . .

Christmas Day

We woke up at . . .

Where we celebrated . . .

Who was there . . .

What we did . . .

Traditions we followed or started . . .

Some of the memorable presents that were
given and received . . .

What we ate and drank . . .

Things that made this Christmas special . . .

Things that made us laugh and smile . . .

What was going on in the wider world?

Reflections & Aspirations

The best moments of the past year . . .

Hopes and wishes for the future . . .

Plans for the coming year . . .

Some of the 'new year' resolutions set . . .

Christmas Present, Christmas Past

Year _____

Christmas Eve

Where we were . . .

Who was there . . .

Things we talked about & things we did . . .

What we were excited about . . .

Things that made the evening memorable . . .

Bedtime was at . . .

Christmas Day

We woke up at . . .

Where we celebrated . . .

Who was there . . .

What we did . . .

Traditions we followed or started . . .

Some of the memorable presents that were
given and received . . .

What we ate and drank . . .

Things that made this Christmas special . . .

Things that made us laugh and smile . . .

What was going on in the wider world?

Reflections & Aspirations

The best moments of the past year . . .

Hopes and wishes for the future . . .

Plans for the coming year . . .

Some of the 'new year' resolutions set . . .

Christmas Present, Christmas Past

Year _____

Christmas Eve

Where we were . . .

Who was there . . .

Things we talked about & things we did . . .

What we were excited about . . .

Things that made the evening memorable . . .

Bedtime was at . . .

Christmas Day

We woke up at . . .

Where we celebrated . . .

Who was there . . .

What we did . . .

Traditions we followed or started . . .

Some of the memorable presents that were
given and received . . .

What we ate and drank . . .

Things that made this Christmas special . . .

Things that made us laugh and smile . . .

What was going on in the wider world?

Reflections & Aspirations

The best moments of the past year . . .

Hopes and wishes for the future . . .

Plans for the coming year . . .

Some of the 'new year' resolutions set . . .

Christmas Present, Christmas Past

Year _____

Christmas Eve

Where we were . . .

Who was there . . .

Things we talked about & things we did . . .

What we were excited about . . .

Things that made the evening memorable . . .

Bedtime was at . . .

Christmas Day

We woke up at . . .

Where we celebrated . . .

Who was there . . .

What we did . . .

Traditions we followed or started . . .

Some of the memorable presents that were given and received . . .

What we ate and drank . . .

Things that made this Christmas special . . .

Things that made us laugh and smile . . .

What was going on in the wider world?

Reflections & Aspirations

The best moments of the past year . . .

Hopes and wishes for the future . . .

Plans for the coming year . . .

Some of the 'new year' resolutions set . . .

Christmas Present, Christmas Past

Year _____

Christmas Eve

Where we were . . .

Who was there . . .

Things we talked about & things we did . . .

What we were excited about . . .

Things that made the evening memorable . . .

Bedtime was at . . .

Christmas Day

We woke up at . . .

Where we celebrated . . .

Who was there . . .

What we did . . .

Traditions we followed or started . . .

Some of the memorable presents that were given and received . . .

What we ate and drank . . .

Things that made this Christmas special . . .

Things that made us laugh and smile . . .

What was going on in the wider world?

Reflections & Aspirations

The best moments of the past year . . .

Hopes and wishes for the future . . .

Plans for the coming year . . .

Some of the 'new year' resolutions set . . .

Christmas Present, Christmas Past

Year _____

Christmas Eve

Where we were . . .

Who was there . . .

Things we talked about & things we did . . .

What we were excited about . . .

Things that made the evening memorable . . .

Bedtime was at . . .

Christmas Day

We woke up at . . .

Where we celebrated . . .

Who was there . . .

What we did . . .

Traditions we followed or started . . .

Some of the memorable presents that were
given and received . . .

What we ate and drank . . .

Things that made this Christmas special . . .

Things that made us laugh and smile . . .

What was going on in the wider world?

Reflections & Aspirations

The best moments of the past year . . .

Hopes and wishes for the future . . .

Plans for the coming year . . .

Some of the 'new year' resolutions set . . .

Christmas Present, Christmas Past

Year _____

Christmas Eve

Where we were . . .

Who was there . . .

Things we talked about & things we did . . .

What we were excited about . . .

Things that made the evening memorable . . .

Bedtime was at . . .

Christmas Day

We woke up at . . .

Where we celebrated . . .

Who was there . . .

What we did . . .

Traditions we followed or started . . .

Some of the memorable presents that were
given and received . . .

What we ate and drank . . .

Things that made this Christmas special . . .

Things that made us laugh and smile . . .

What was going on in the wider world?

Reflections & Aspirations

The best moments of the past year . . .

Hopes and wishes for the future . . .

Plans for the coming year . . .

Some of the 'new year' resolutions set . . .

Christmas Present, Christmas Past

Year _____

Christmas Eve

Where we were . . .

Who was there . . .

Things we talked about & things we did . . .

What we were excited about . . .

Things that made the evening memorable . . .

Bedtime was at . . .

Christmas Day

We woke up at . . .

Where we celebrated . . .

Who was there . . .

What we did . . .

Traditions we followed or started . . .

Some of the memorable presents that were
given and received . . .

What we ate and drank . . .

Things that made this Christmas special . . .

Things that made us laugh and smile . . .

What was going on in the wider world?

Reflections & Aspirations

The best moments of the past year . . .

Hopes and wishes for the future . . .

Published by **FROM YOU TO ME**

For a full range of all our titles where journals &
books can also be personalised, please visit

WWW.FROMYOUTOME.COM

Christmas Present,
Christmas Past

Sketch collection first published by Journals Of A Lifetime, an imprint of
FROM YOU TO ME LTD, in January 2009.

This version published May 2019.

Designed, published and printed in the UK.

This paper is manufactured from pulp sourced from forests that are legally
and sustainably managed.

For permission requests, contact the publisher at their head office address:

FROM YOU TO ME
Waterhouse
Waterhouse Lane
Monkton Combe
Bath, BA2 7JA, UK

HELLO@FROMYOUTOME.COM
WWW.FROMYOUTOME.COM